BT BODMIN (RLY) 22.4.92

CORN...
CHINA-CLA...

John R
Cornwall Arch
Cornwall Co

C000176502

INTRODUCTION

THE EXTRACTION of china-clay dominates mid-Cornwall, and is today a powerful economic force in the county. Its importance is recent in historic terms, but this century has outstripped and eclipsed Cornwall's traditional industries of hard-rock mining and fishing. Only tourism and agriculture now compete as major employers.

Yet few of the visitors who pour into the county each year are aware of the china-clay district north of St Austell, other than as an eerie landscape glimpsed from the A30 as they traverse Goss Moor. Unless they live or work in the district, Cornish residents are also likely to shun the uplands where the 'white gold' is king. Smaller china-clay workings on Bodmin Moor, West Penwith, or in Devon, are equally little-known.

While there has been an upsurge of interest in recent years in the remains of Cornwall's industrial past, with mines, old railways, water mills and quarries all receiving close attention, the china-clay industry has by comparison been neglected. In many respects this is understandable, as the industry is still very much an active one, and members of the public cannot be encouraged to wander into modern workings. Nonetheless, the extraction of china-clay is now well over two hundred years old, and has created its own unique and fascinating industrial landscapes; many of these can be explored from public footpaths or are visible from the road. Not all the active china-clay district is yet despoiled, and for the lover of little known industrial by-ways (often reclaimed by nature) the clay uplands have a great deal to offer.

CHINA-CLAY is decomposed granite. To be precise, it is granite where the feldspar crystals have changed to kaolin, a fine white clay, leaving the quartz and mica in the rock unchanged. This process happened long ago in geological time, and affected only certain parts of the granite uplands in Devon and Cornwall. Kaolin is found on western Dartmoor, Bodmin Moor, the Hensbarrow Moors north of St Austell, Tregonning Hill, and West Penwith. Here, granite near the surface is exposed not as a solid rock but as a soft **growan**, a gravel-like deposit of quartz sand mixed with mica and china-clay.

The clay found little use until the mid-18th century, as it was difficult to separate from the matrix of quartz sand, and it lacked the natural plasticity of a good potting clay. Its main property is an exceptional resistance to heat. Refractory clays, as heat resistant types are known, were ideal for the lining of tin-smelting furnaces and there is some evidence that china-clay was being worked on Hensbarrow, perhaps for this purpose, as early as 1584.

In China, kaolin had been used since AD700 to create a particularly fine type of pottery: porcelain. The manufacture of this hard white ware requires the use not only of china-clay or kaolin, but also the addition in exact proportions of ground china-stone. China-stone, or petuntse as it was called in China, is granite that has been only partially altered by the process of kaolinisation, and is quarried like any other rock. The mixture of china-clay and stone was fired at high temperature, when the ground stone vitrified and gave great strength to the finished pottery. The resulting porcelain could be very thin, delicate, and translucent.

In the early 18th century, European pottery was by contrast somewhat coarse, even if elaborately glazed and decorated. European potters had attempted to discover the secrets of the fine white ware from the East since it had first been imported in quantity after 1600. All attempts to reproduce it in Britain had failed, as there was no understanding of the exact nature of the materials required.

The discovery of the huge reserves of china-clay and stone in Cornwall was made by William Cookworthy around 1746. Cookworthy (1705-1780) was a Quaker and a chemist by profession. Born in Kingsbridge,

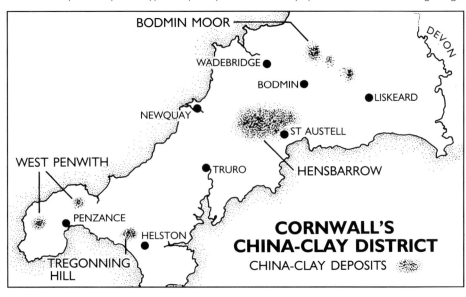

BODMIN MOOR

DEVON

WADEBRIDGE ●

BODMIN ●

● LISKEARD

NEWQUAY ●

● ST AUSTELL

WEST PENWITH

● TRURO

HENSBARROW

PENZANCE

● HELSTON

TREGONNING HILL

CORNWALL'S CHINA-CLAY DISTRICT

CHINA-CLAY DEPOSITS

Women workers ('Bal Maidens') beside a linhay with blocks of dried china-clay   *Photo: ECCI*

Devon, he had set up as a wholesale chemist in Plymouth. Fascinated by geology and the nature of porcelain, he obtained samples of china-clay for his experiments from the Americas, little realising that a superior source of the same ingredients lay much closer to home. Sometime in 1745 or '46, Cookworthy took the opportunity during one of his regular visits to Cornwall to prospect for china-clay.

He found the materials he was searching for at Tregonning Hill (between Helston and Marazion), and then, in greater quantity, at Carloggas near St Stephen-in-Brannel. Cookworthy did not, as has sometimes been implied, first discover the existence of china-clay in Britain. His recognition of these materials was new only for the connection he made with them and their potential for porcelain manufacture; china-stone had been quarried since Tudor times for use as a building material, and without existing quarries Cookworthy would have been unable to assess the clay and stone in depth. Over subsequent years Cookworthy experimented with porcelain manufacture using Cornish materials, and in 1768 took out a patent. A factory was set up in Plymouth, which was later moved to Bristol, and despite producing commercial quantities of porcelain was always

in financial difficulties. The problems of large-scale production were difficult to resolve.

Cookworthy passed the patent to his partner Richard Champion in 1774, and relinquished his interest in the business. The potters of Staffordshire, led by Josiah Wedgwood, then took a great interest in Cornish clay and stone. They opposed the renewal of Cookworthy's patent by Champion, and sought to gain supplies of the china-clay and stone for themselves. The result, after a legal battle in 1775, was that Champion lost his monopoly over the Cornish materials; from then on all the potters were free to make their bargains with landowners and to lease their own setts. During the late 18th and early 19th centuries, control of the Hensbarrow china-clay pits and quarries passed to the Staffordshire potters.

This remote control of a local industry could not last for long. Inevitably, the problems caused by their distance from Cornwall led the potters to relinquish their interest to local entrepreneurs, and the extraction of china-clay became a Cornish business. By the middle of the 19th century, china-clay production was in the hands of a multitude of small companies all selling their products on the open market, a market that was by then rapidly expanding.

THE FIRST PITS

BY 1800 there were several china-clay pits and quarries active on Hensbarrow, but these were very small and shallow in comparison with today's workings. Pits and quarries known to have been in production at this date include Carloggas Moor, Trethosa, Treviscoe, Trelavour Downs, Hendra Downs, Gonnamarris, and Goonvean. Whereas a modern pit, often the direct descendant of one of these early excavations, may be several acres in extent and three to four hundred feet deep, in 1807 Trethosa was one of the largest works but only about nine feet deep. It produced just 300 tons per annum. Part of the reason for this low output was that the industry was remarkably labour-intensive, in an age when Cornish hard-rock mining for tin and copper was at its peak and competing for the same workforce. There was very little mechanisation of china-clay processing until the later part of the 19th century, as the profits to be made from clay were small compared with the riches that might be gained from metal ores. The canny entrepreneurs of St Austell were quick to realise that although profits might be less spectacular, they were steady; and an assured income from clay was often preferable to an uncertain one from copper.

Clay pits in these early times were shallow and avoided the cost of pumping, which was to be of prime importance in later years as pits deepened. Shallow pits also suited the primitive methods of waste disposal then in use. Little in the way of fixed equipment or permanent structures was required by the industry in this period. If pumping was mechanised at all, it would be by using a waterwheel and bucket-lift pump. The processing of the finished clay was a lengthy and labour-intensive process, relying on the natural agency of wind and sun to dry the slurry to a marketable condition. Dr Fitton, visiting the Hensbarrow uplands in 1807, wrote:

The overburden having been removed to a considerable extent, the clay itself is dug progressively in steps, the discoloured portions being picked out and thrown away.

The selected clay is then wheeled to the washing place or strake, and washed with a stream of water. A large quantity of sand is at once separated, and this is shovelled away continually. The clay and finer mica are carried on by the flowing stream to pits and ponds, which are rectangular receptacles built of rough stone, cemented by lime; the pits are five or six feet in the side and four feet deep, the ponds 20 feet by 12 feet and of the same depth. The first pit receives the fine sand and coarser mica, the second, and perhaps the third, the fine mica, while the fine clay settles in the last or passes on to the ponds. When the ponds are full their contents are transferred to shallow pans lined with granite, about 40 feet by 12 feet and from 14 to 18 inches deep. In these pans it remains from four to eight months, often from September to the following May. It is by that time stiff enough to be cut up into square blocks, which are further dried by exposure to the sun, scraped and rammed into casks. The scrapings and waste are wheeled back to the strake and re-washed.

This is an excellent description of the industry in its fledgling period. The business of extraction was more akin to an agricultural process than an industrial one, with the finished clay stacked in neatly thatched ricks, after the yearly spring and summer 'savings'.

From an advertisement of 1889

STREAM AND STRAKE

THESE PIONEER clay workers had first to find their clay. The method used was the same as in prospecting for other minerals, such as tin and copper; a series of small pits was dug across the ground. Where the indications from these prospecting pits were favourable, a lease of the **sett** was obtained from the landowner, and operations could commence. First the **overburden**, or surface soil and peat was removed. Below this the discoloured china-clay, stained with iron, would be discarded, and extraction proper could then commence.

The early method of working is known as **stream and strake**, and was as described by Dr Fitton. First a water supply had to be obtained, usually by diverting a stream across the moorland to the works. Miles of leats to carry water are a legacy of this technique on Bodmin Moor. The stream was directed over the exposed clay ground, washing the kaolin-ised material away from the unaltered rocks or **stent**. Workers using shovels and short picks (**dubbers**) stood in the clay stream and broke up the material; as the water deepened the channel in the working face it formed a gully or strake. In the early phase of extraction hillside sites were chosen for preference and the clay

flowed by gravity to the process area; as the pit deepened and this was no longer possible, it was necessary either to drive an adit from the bottom of the pit on a hillside site or sink a shaft from the top through which the clay was pumped to surface.

The first pumps used were simple plunger devices made from hollowed logs and opera-ted by hand. While the depth of the openwork was shallow this sufficed, but as the works deepened and expanded a water wheel would be installed to drive a series of lift pumps, similar to those used in underground tin and copper mines.

Pumping the clay from the bottom of the pit to the ponds and lagoons where it was to be dried was one problem. Another, also very familiar to Cornwall's tin and copper miners, was the disposal of waste material. The production of china-clay involves the creation of vast amounts of waste sand, gravel, and rock, which have to be removed from the pit and dumped. The average debris ratio is 8:1, so for even with the modest production of 2000 tons in 1800, 16,000 tons of waste had to be dealt with. Primary separation of the heavier waste elements took place in the

Waterwheel at Carloggas, driving flat-rods to a distant pump   *Photo: ECCI*

strake itself, the men removing the **stent** (rocks) as they worked. Coarse gravel and sand was eliminated from the clay stream before pumping to surface by running it through a series of pits, the gravel depositing in them and the clay running off the top. At intervals the stream would be diverted to another pit and the waste material dug out. These gravel pits in time became more sophisticated and incorporated a certain amount of mechanisation to speed emptying, but the basic principle remained unchanged until recent years.

Disposal of these wastes from shallow workings was originally done by **shammelling**, the material being dug by hand and thrown back up a series of stepped excavation platforms. The shammelling technique was another very strong incentive to keep pits shallow in the early days of the industry. This back-breaking labour was eventually replaced by mechanical haulage up a tramway incline or skip-road, power being provided by a horse-whim, water-wheel, or steam engine. The wastes were barrowed out along flat topped dumps that spread, fan-like, from the margins of the excavation to cover the nearby moor. Barrows were in time replaced by tramways and hand-pushed skips to speed this process. These **finger dumps** were a notable feature of many early clayworks (and also stone quarries), but very few survive today. As the number of producers increased and many small companies began to compete for the same productive areas, clay producers could no longer afford to be so profligate with land and dumping methods changed.

Once the clay stream had reached the processing area beside or above the pit, the fine quartz sand and mica was removed. The original method of separation involved the use of three rectangular catch-pits, stepped one below the other; as the stream flowed through the pits the waste was deposited in each, sand in the first, fine sand and some mica in the second, and mica only in the third. The stream was then allowed to flow to settling pits for thickening. Overseeing operations was the 'Captain', or foreman of the works, whose badge of office was the inevitable bowler hat.

The period of transition: an air dry on the right with a small, early pan-kiln on the left   *Photo: ECCI*

AIR DRYS, CARTS, AND NEW HARBOURS

BEFORE the clay could be transported to the Potteries it had to be dried. The first step was to run the clay stream into stone-lined settling pits; these might be rectangular or circular in shape. Here the clay settled to the bottom of the pit and the clear top water was drawn off through **pin-hole launders**, square wooden pipes set vertically in the pits. Connected to a drain, holes in the launder could be unplugged from the top, and the clear water above the settling clay was removed. When the clay had thickened by the required amount it was **landed** or run off via a sluice in the base of the tank to the next stage in the process. The clay ran on to shallow clay pans dug on the open moors, and dried gradually in the open air. When dry enough to be cut into blocks it was removed and stacked in open-sided sheds or air drys till ready for sale.

This method of air-drying, used in places until the 1920s, was inevitably slow and required much heavy labour. The wet Cornish climate restricted production to two **savings** a year, and in winter it would take some eight months to prepare the finished clay. Despite the essentially rural and small-scale nature of the industry in these early years, enough clay and stone was produced to impose a strain on the roads and harbours of the St Austell area. There was no home market within the county for china-clay; later attempts to set up potteries in Cornwall met with little success, as the coal needed to fire the kilns had to be imported and this made the process uneconomic. Even the clay production of 2000 tons per annum (this represents some 700 wagonloads) in the early years of the 19th century meant the export of this tonnage over roads that were little better than cart tracks.

When the wagons eventually reached the coast, there were no adequate harbour facilities. Along the south coast of Cornwall it was common practise to run ships up onto the beach at high tide, load from the carts when the tide fell, and sail off on the next flood. Such methods were inconvenient and often dangerous if there was a change in the weather. There was no alternative to transport by sea; no canals connected Cornwall with the rest of Britain, and the main-line railway was not to arrive until 1859.

The first new harbour was Charlestown. Built by Charles Rashleigh in a little cove at West Polmear, south of St Austell, it was started in 1791. By 1796 at *Mr C Rashleigh's new quay great quantities of the china stone or decomposed granite from St Stephens about 5 miles north of St Austle (sic) were laying to be shipped for Liverpool or to be sent to Worcestershire and Staffordshire for the Porcelain Ware*. (from Hatchett's Diary).

The construction of other harbours to serve the clay industry would have been delayed into the middle of the 19th century, had it not been for the boom in copper mining around St Austell after 1820. New ports were built that could export not only china-clay and stone, but also copper ore to the smelters of South Wales, with coal for the engines of the mines forming a return cargo. Pentewan was the first of these, built by Sir Charles Hawkins from

China-clay aristocracy: the Martyn family of Carthew and Wheal Martyn   *Photo: ECCI*

Charlestown Harbour from the air   *Photo: CAU*

1817 to 1826. Although never a particularly successful harbour, as its entrance was plagued with silting problems, Pentewan was significant for another reason. It was the first china-clay port to be linked by rail to its hinterland, when a horse tramway was built from St Austell to Pentewan, opening in 1829.

Charlestown and Pentewan were welcome additions to the anchorages available to the shippers of china-clay, but they were still limited in their capacity and had difficult entrances to negotiate. The next harbour to be built was not primarily intended for the export of china-clay, but for copper ore; Par, constructed on a rocky beach by J T Treffry from 1829 to 1840, was connected by canal to the Fowey Consols mine inland. The harbour became important for china-clay after 1842, when a horse tramway was built through the Luxulyan Valley and into the clay district around Bugle. Another tramway was built by Treffry from Hendra, near St Dennis, to the fishing village of Newquay on the north coast, and completed in 1849. By this time, the china-clay industry stood on the brink of extensive change.

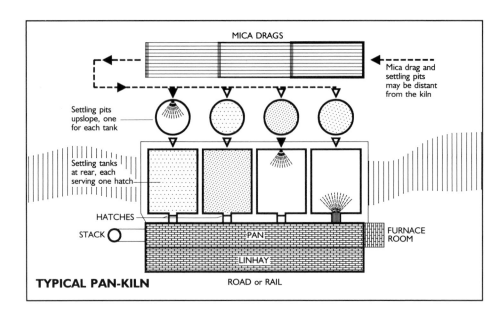

MICA DRAGS

Mica drag and settling pits may be distant from the kiln

Settling pits upslope, one for each tank

Settling tanks at rear, each serving one hatch

HATCHES

STACK

PAN

FURNACE ROOM

LINHAY

TYPICAL PAN-KILN   ROAD or RAIL

A LARGE part of the cost of china-clay to the potter has always been transport; unlike tin, clay was (and is) a product of low intrinsic value per ton. The improvement of the transport systems in the St Austell area lowered the price, and created a demand for clay that the producers were increasingly unable to fulfil. While more labour could be used to speed the process of extraction, the drying of the finished clay could not be hastened in the damp and misty Cornish climate. During the years from 1820 to 1850, local business people or **adventurers** had invested in new clay companies and pits, but production had only increased from 2000 tons per annum to some 13000 tons by 1838.

By 1840 there was a pressing need for better methods. In Staffordshire, **Slip-kilns** had been in use for over a century to dry wet-ground flint, and these must have come to the attention of Cornish clay-producers on their travels to the Potteries. Many in the industry doubted the practicality of using artificial methods to dry the clay, claiming that its quality would be compromised. There was also the cost of coal to be considered, if kilns were to be introduced. In the event, the first pan-kilns to be built, at Greensplat and Parkandillack in 1845, were a great success and

Truscott's Kiln at Parkandillack, one of the earliest pan-kilns, built c.1846   *Photo: John R Smith*

other producers quickly followed suit. These first kilns were very small, but even so could dry a charge of clay in three days. At a stroke the major obstacle to increased production was removed, as is well illustrated by the

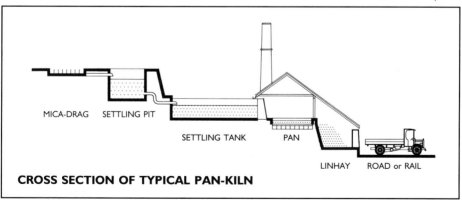

MICA-DRAG   SETTLING PIT

SETTLING TANK   PAN

LINHAY   ROAD or RAIL

CROSS SECTION OF TYPICAL PAN-KILN

Cross section of a typical Pan-Kiln. Most pan-kilns make use of the natural slope to move the clay through the process. Settling pits and tanks provide primary and secondary de-watering and the pan dries the clay ready for storage in the linhay.

Settling tanks at the rear of a kiln at Carvear   *Photo: Wheal Martyn Museum*

increase in production between 1838 (13440 tons) and 1858 (65600 tons).

The design was simple, echoing the principle of the old Roman bath-house, with its hypocaust or heated floor. A furnace at one end of the building was connected to a chimney stack at the other by a series of brick flues running beneath a tiled floor. The tiles on the floor, or *pan*, were porous. At the rear of the kiln or *dry* were a series of stone-lined settling tanks into which the clay slurry was run and allowed to settle, the clear water being drawn off from the top at intervals. When the clay had thickened to the consistency of a thick cream it was run onto the floor of the pan through hatch doors, and spread to an even thickness. The hot flue gases drew the moisture from the clay through the porous tiles and out through the stack in a white plume. Below the pan was the *linhay* or storage area, into which the clay was shovelled when dry.

Pan-kilns developed quickly during the 1860s and 1870s into a standard form. Kilns, also known simply as 'drys' in the St Austell area, became a familiar and integral part of the landscape, often situated many miles from the producing clay-pit and connected to it by pipeline. The asymmetric roof covering a squat profile, the use of natural stone and slate, and the punctuating stack made them a truly vernacular feature of the clay district.

Improved processing methods were not confined solely to the drying of the clay. The mica and sand were also now removed more effectively by using *drags*, rather than the old catch-pits. The principle of the drags was to direct the clay stream through a series of long channels, separated by boards or, in later years, concrete dividers; by constructing these with a very shallow gradient, the liquid clay was slowed and the solid wastes deposited in the bottom of the channels. At intervals the clay stream would be diverted to a fresh channel in the drag, bungs were removed from drain holes in the base of the channel, and the waste material was flushed away. The waste mica and fine sand were usually dumped in the nearest stream or river, which all ran white in the St Austell district. This had two immediate results: the destruction of all aquatic life in the river, and the silting-up of ports and harbours such as Pentewan. The mica waste in the rivers still contained significant amounts of clay, which led to the establishment of many small *mica-works* downstream of the large producers. These local entrepreneurs would choose a suitable spot on the river, erect a little kiln, and divert the stream into their settling tanks. In this way they could reprocess the waste and extract a second-grade clay.

COOKWORTHY'S discoveries in the mid-18th century had led to the gradual expansion of what was in 1800 a very localised and small scale industry, producing less than 2000 tons per annum, and 65,600 tons by 1858; this then rose to over 550,00 tons a year by the turn of the century. By far the greater part of this output came from the St Austell district, although deposits had been recognised in granite areas elsewhere in the county: at Leswidden and Towednack in Penwith, at the original site on Tregonning Hill (Wheal Grey), and in Devon on Lee Moor. In the 1860s, china-clay deposits on Bodmin Moor had also been found and were to be exploited despite difficulties with their high mica content. Of these areas, only Hensbarrow and Lee Moor were to prove of major significance in the long-term development of the industry, although there are still two active pits on Bodmin Moor, and one small one in West Penwith.

In 1858 there were 89 active china-clay works; by 1914 this number had increased to 159. Many of these were small pits, controlled by individual companies. Each of these producers had their own arrangements for the marketing, transport and shipping of their products; each had its own strictly defined sett boundaries, within which it had to undertake the extraction

and processing of its clay, and the disposal of its waste products. Inevitably this led to the dumping of waste rock and sand on good clay ground, to a duplication and proliferation of

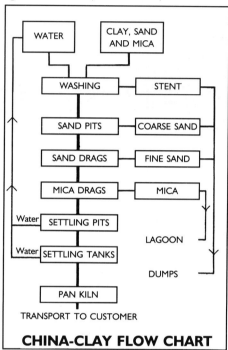

CHINA-CLAY FLOW CHART

A set of mica-drags

Photo: ECCI

DECENNIAL PRODUCTION
CHINA-CLAY AND STONE, 1810–1910

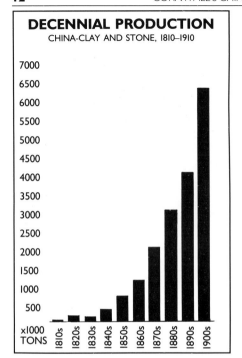

process areas, and to an increasing pressure on the landscape as pits deepened and widened. The china-clay workers could no longer afford to be so wasteful with their ground as they had been in the old days; methods of extraction and dumping had to change to suit the new order.

If pits could no longer expand sideways, they had to deepen. This meant greater problems with pumping the clay stream to surface, unless the company was fortunate and could dig their

pit into a hillside, where the process area could be connected directly to the bottom of the pit by a tunnel, or **adit**. More often than not, this method was impractical. Instead, a shaft was sunk on the edge of the clay ground, and an adit driven from the bottom of this to a point below the centre of the intended work area. A **rise** was then driven up to the surface, by now stripped of overburden, and a button-hole launder placed in this shaft. Essentially the same as the square launders used in settling pits and tanks but with wooden patches nailed over the holes rather than plugs, this reached from the sump to the top of the rise. The top patch was removed to allow the clay stream to flow through the adit to the pumping shaft, and as the pit deepened so further patches were removed.

A waterwheel was often used to pump the clay stream from the bottom of the shaft. If water were unavailable in sufficient quantity on site to drive a wheel for pumping, this could be sited some distance away and the drive transmitted from a crank via a series of reciprocating iron rods, or **flat rods**. Water power is unreliable during the summer months, and large producers soon found that they needed a more dependable technology, despite the additional expense. Cornish beam engines were commonplace on tin and copper mines, and from the 1850s were adopted by the china-clay industry for pumping and winding waste sand out of the larger pits.

The old finger dumps were also abandoned in favour of a neater, less land-hungry approach. If dumps could no longer spread horizontally across the moor, then they must go upwards;

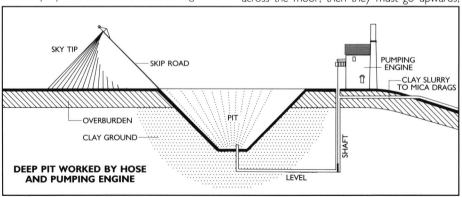

DEEP PIT WORKED BY HOSE AND PUMPING ENGINE

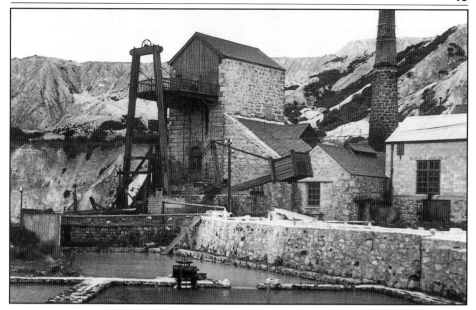

West Gunheath engine house

Photo: Frank Woodall

soon, new **sky-tips** were created by hauling waste out of the pits up an inclined plane of rails. Instead of transferring the sand out to flat-topped burrows it was tipped directly off the top of the incline, which was gradually extended as the tip grew. These pyramidal dumps rapidly became a trademark of the Hensbarrow area, creating the 'Cornish Alps' that have intrigued so many summer visitors.

China-clay casks on a horse-drawn wagon near Carthew   *Photo: Wheal Martyn Museum*

The driving force behind the rapid expansion of the industry during this, the latter half of the 19th century, was a multitude of new uses for the clay itself. No longer just a material of interest to the Staffordshire potters, china-clay was by now an essential part of papermaking, the sizing of cotton goods, paint manufacture and cosmetics. Of these, the papermakers were by far the most important . The clay was despatched mostly in lump form, but for some overseas markets it was packed into wooden casks of five or ten hundredweights capacity. Many cooperages were set up in the St Austell area to satisfy this demand.

As the industry entered the 20th century, the landscape of Hensbarrow had become transformed into a unique and extraordinary patchwork of small pits, conical dumps, settling pits and tanks. The chimneys of engine houses and pan-kilns punctuated this landscape, whose bare upland aspect was relieved only by the deeply wooded valleys of the Fal, Barn, Gover, Trenance, and Par rivers. No less fascinating were the names of the clay companies and pits: Lantern, Wheal Frederick, Anchor, Imperial Goonbarrow, Plain Dealing, and Poor Man's Friend.

RAILWAYS AND PIPELINES

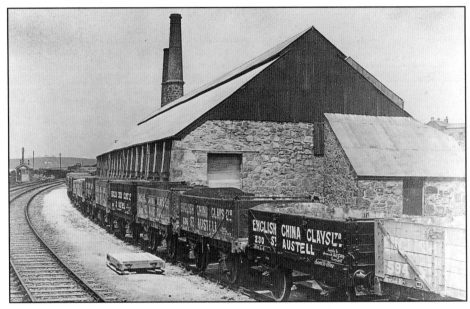

Kilns and railway wagons at Kernick in the 1920s

Photo: ECCI

ALTHOUGH by 1850 the clay producers of Hensbarrow were served by three horse tramways (the Pentewan Railway, the Par to Bugle tramway and the Hendra to Newquay tramway), only two of these penetrated the clay district itself. Their capacity and speed was little better than the roads that they supplemented, roads that by this time were choked with teams of horses hauling wagons to the coast. Other parts of the county had the new steam railways like the Bodmin and Wadebridge or the West Cornwall Railway, but the tramways could not be converted to steam traction without costly civil engineering works on a large scale.

The opening of the broad gauge Cornwall Railway in 1859 at last gave the county a through route to the rest of Britain across the Tamar bridge, and this new railway passed close to the southern edge of the china-clay district at St Austell and Par. In 1869 the Cornwall Junction Railway was opened from the main line at Burngullow to Drinnick Mill,

where there was easy access to many important pits. Another was the Lostwithiel and Fowey Railway, opened in the same year, giving a route from the pits to the coast (via Burngullow, St Austell, Lostwithiel and Fowey) without transhipment.

The qualities of Fowey as a deep-water harbour had long been evident, but without good transport links it had previously played no part in the shipping of china-clay. The broad gauge rail link enjoyed a brief flurry of activity, but another scheme was soon to steal its traffic. Between 1872 and 1874 the old Treffry Tramway system was rebuilt and extended as a modern steam railway; new rails were laid through the Luxulyan Valley, and the line was extended to Fowey direct from Par. Branches were built to Carbis, Wheal Rose, Retew, and to Drinnick Mill (from the north). Known as the Cornwall Minerals Railway (CMR), the new lines were of course standard gauge, and could not connect or directly interchange traffic with the Cornwall Junction Railway. A magnificent new headquarters and works was built at St Blazey for the new company by Sir Morton Peto, the last great Victorian railway engineer and contractor, who was ruined financially by this contract and was forced to sell his wife's jewellery as a result. The CMR quickly captured the clay traffic from the broad gauge company, as their new route to Fowey was shorter, and they also had a direct route to Par dock. Fowey developed rapidly as the major deep-water china-clay port, a position it holds to this day.

By 1895 the Cornwall Railway had become part of the Great Western Railway, and had absorbed all the CMR lines; the broad gauge was no more. A new line was built from Bugle to Gunheath in 1893, and the Retew branch was extended to Melbur in 1912. The last line to be built in the St Austell district was the Trenance Valley Branch, opened in 1920. All these railways carried heavy traffic, with small tank engines struggling up the steep grades on rails greasy with clay. The trucks they hauled were painted with the owning company's livery, the names of North and Rose, West of England, and Great Treverbyn jostling for position as the train panted and rattled its way under the bridge at Slip Siding. For the clay producers, a new age had dawned; pan-kilns

were built beside the railways or had sidings laid into them. Some pits, like Goonvean, now had a direct rail connection. Where the pit was distant from the railway, pipelines were laid to new kilns, as at Burngullow where Frank Parkyn built a line of drys a quarter of a mile long. Despite these attempts to improve communications in the area, until well into the 20th century large quantities of china-clay were still moved laboriously from the works high on the Hensbarrow Moors to Charlestown and Par by horse-drawn waggons. Streets in St Austell were slick with a fine white mud, congested by the waggoners and their three-horse teams.

Nowhere else in the county were railways built exclusively to serve the clay industry, but china-clay provided a vital traffic for several lines that had been built for other reasons. On Bodmin Moor the use of pipelines to carry clay down to the railways became a universal practise. The Wenford branch of the old Bodmin and Wadebridge Railway carried clay from the pits at Durfold, and after 1900, Stannon; kilns were built beside the GWR main line at Bodmin Road; and a kiln at Moorswater near Liskeard provided new traffic for the Looe branch.

Bugle station with railway wagons being loaded from the wharf   *Photo: ECCI*

STONE MILLS AND BRICKWORKS

CHINA-CLAY now had a market far beyond the Potteries of Staffordshire, but the only use for china-stone was to remain in porcelain manufacture. China-stone quarries on Hensbarrow had not been subject to the degree of technological change that had swept the clay pits; the stone was quarried in traditional fashion, using gunpowder to **heave** the blocks from the working face, which were then broken up by hand and the stone shipped in lump form direct to the potters. All the major clay producers had their own china-stone quarries, often attached to the clay-pit in the early days. After 1850 the best stone quarries became localised in the area of Rostowrack Downs, near Nanpean. The working of china-stone involves not merely its quarrying and subsequent crushing, but the grinding of the lump stone into a fine powder. The potters then mixed this powder with water to form a **slip**, suitable for applying to the ware as a glaze or for mixing with china-clay in the manufacture of high-grade porcelain. The potters always insisted on having the best stone in lump form so that they could assess its quality, before grinding it in their own mills.

From around 1870 stone mills were built in Cornwall to grind the poorer grades of china-stone. This stone was dried, bagged, and shipped to the Potteries for use in cheaper varieties of pottery and stoneware. These stone mills were massive structures, and took advantage of the abundant water-power available in the deep valleys below the moorland areas. The construction of the mills followed a distinctive pattern, although there were differences of detail. A central wheelpit was flanked by a mill building on either side, though often under a common roof; horizontal shafts driven off the hub of the wheel ran in tunnels beneath the floor of the grinding house. Vertical shafts were driven from the main shaft by means of large bevel gears, and these rotated in the centre of the circular grinding pans on the upper floor. The pans, normally one or two on each side of the wheelpit, were built with granite sides and floored with china-stone **pavers**. Attached to the rotating shaft inside the pan were four iron arms, or **gates**; these pushed large blocks of stone, the **runners**, around the base of the pan.

In operation, lump china-stone was carted or

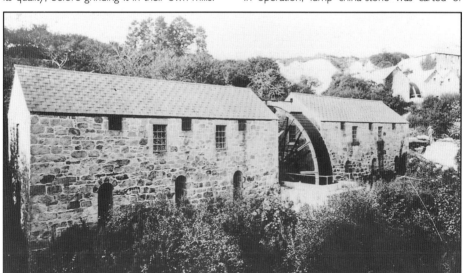

Tregargus china-stone mills

trammed into the rear of the mill. It was then knapped by hand to a smaller size, before being loaded into the pans; the pans were then filled with water, as this was a wet-grinding process. The waterwheel was set in motion, and as the gates and runners rotated, so the stone was ground to a creamy slurry. The grinding would normally last for 24 hours; the slurry was then run off into a pan-kiln, dried, and bagged. Sometimes the kiln would be attached to the mill, but could be located elsewhere with the slurry sent to it through a pipeline. China-stone production rose from 11600 tons in 1850 to 68174 tons by 1907, and for a time stone-milling was a distinctive part of the Cornish industrial scene.

The china-stone mills tended to be hidden from view in wooded valleys, beside the streams that fed their waterwheels; another part of the industrial picture was often equally disguised by the chimneys of pan-kilns surrounding it. In amongst the clay pits and dumps were the brickworks, which found a use for clay that otherwise would have been discarded. This clay was discoloured by iron-staining, or was of inferior quality in other respects. While brickmaking was never of great economic importance in Cornwall, and few bricks made in the county were exported to other parts of Britain, it was for a time a significant local industry in the china-clay districts. The original deposit at Tregonning Hill was only used for brickmaking after 1880; and there were many other clay pits that proved unsuitable for anything but brickmaking. Some clay producers combined both activities on the one site, adding a brickworks to their existing process areas. Bricks

made from china-clay had the property of being exceptionally heat-resistant, or naturally refractory; they were thus in great demand from the mining industry for boiler-houses, calciners, and smelting furnaces. After 1850, the use of the pan-kiln itself created a large demand within the clay industry for bricks and tiles. Many brickworks were fully occupied supplying this local trade, as the furnaces and pans of the drys had to be regularly rebuilt.

The bricks were not pure china-clay, but a mixture of clay, quartz, and fine sand, fired at high temperature. The brick kilns in the china-clay districts were usually simple down-draught types, where the bricks were stacked inside a circular chamber and fired from an external furnace. Many china-clay bricks were discoloured by iron, and burnt to a pale buff or pink; some were a white or cream colour, and as white bricks were fashionable in late Victorian times, these also found their way into domestic architecture.

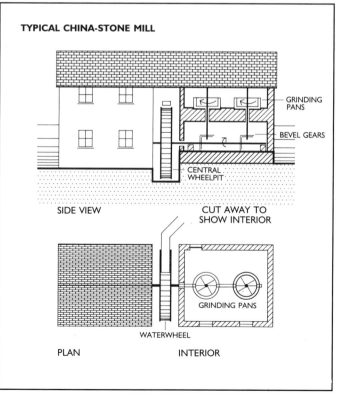

TYPICAL CHINA-STONE MILL

GRINDING PANS

BEVEL GEARS

CENTRAL WHEELPIT

SIDE VIEW

CUT AWAY TO SHOW INTERIOR

GRINDING PANS

WATERWHEEL

PLAN

INTERIOR

Par Brickworks, c1900; the bricks are stacked to dry in the long 'hacks' before firing in the kiln   *S Colwill*

Interior of a working clay dry, about 1910; clay slurry is being tipped from a wagon on the travelling bridge, onto the heated kiln floor

THE GROWTH of the china-clay industry was accompanied by a corresponding growth in the workforce that served it. Soon, the moorland villages of St Stephen, St Dennis and Roche were outgrown and overcrowded, as miners and quarrymen were recruited from all over Cornwall to work in the new pits. On Bodmin Moor the industry was never intensive enough to create a similar pressure; but in the St Austell area, new housing and new settlements sprang up to house a new generation of Cornish miners. For many who had worked in tin and copper, clay working was felt to be demeaning and less skilled than the extraction of metal ores. Earnings, too, were generally well below the pay that an experienced hard rock miner could expect. Nonetheless, employment in china-clay was very often welcome to men who otherwise would have faced only the prospect of unemployment or emigration, as first copper, then tin, withered and died in the face of foreign competition.

The result, in the late 19th and early 20th centuries, was the creation of a distinctive mining community in new villages that spread across the moors, terraces of grey cottages springing up where only goats had grazed the coarse and windswept grass. Settlements such as Stenalees, Bugle, Foxhole, Whitemoor and Treviscoe are all products of this time. The new communities required not only houses but places of worship and education; miles from the old parish churches, every village soon had its Wesleyan or United Methodist chapel. Often these incorporated a Sunday school at the side or rear. Compulsory full-time education followed, and elementary schools appeared in most villages, often segregated with boys and girls on either side of the building. St Austell itself was now a boom town, and had outgrown its centre around the church. New offices, banks and stores in the town served a rash of terraced housing in Bethel, Mount Charles, and Holmbush; and the villas of wealthy clay company owners appeared on the wooded slopes above them. The clay companies on occasion built housing

for their workers at the pit itself. Virginia, Karslake, and Goonamarth had severe terraces built in isolation from any other cottages, miles from the nearest shops or school. Meanwhile, the older farms and hamlets of the moors were facing annihilation as the clay pits and dumps advanced across the landscape.

Engine houses at Dubbers pit; the new house in the foreground was built in 1905   *Photo: ECCI*

AS THE china-clay industry entered the 20th century, more changes in technology and organisation were required to keep pace with demand in a trade that was now world-wide (seventy-five percent of the clay was shipped abroad by 1912). The old stream and strake working in the pits was replaced by high-pressure hoses to wash the clay from the stopes; the first use of a high-pressure hose was by the West of England Company in 1877, but this experiment was sabotaged by angry workers. Special high-speed pumps were subsequently developed for this purpose, often fed from older flooded workings. By the mid 1920s this method was accepted practice in the Hensbarrow area. Electricity, pioneered for industrial use in St Austell during the 1880s, could now power centrifugal pumps to lift the clay slurry itself, although the day when they would replace the beam engine was still some way off. Power houses containing oil or gas engines and generators became a feature of the pits, and overhead cables added to the visual clutter of stacks, launders, and cableways. In 1936 a large coal-fired power station was built by ECLP at Drinnick, serving the entire Hensbarrow area. A less spectacular but nonetheless significant change was the introduction in 1911 of filter presses as an adjunct to the pan kiln; the presses removed most of the water from the clay before it was placed on the pan, effecting great savings in coal.

The growing demand for the products of the industry was curtailed by the effects of two world wars, during both of which the clay industry came almost to a standstill as export markets disappeared. The Great War and the trade depression of the 1930s created pressure on the industry to rationalise and modernise its production methods. It had become obvious that the multitude of small companies was now a barrier to the efficient working of the clay ground, as deposits had now been located underneath old dumps placed on ground previously regarded as barren. To expand existing pits was impossible where they adjoined land leased by separate companies.

In 1919 an amalgamation of three large companies (Martin Brothers, the West of England and Great Beam Company, and the North Cornwall China Clay Company) produced English China Clays Ltd, or ECC, controlling 50% of the industry's production. This process of consolidation was continued in 1932 by the formation of English Clays, Lovering, Pochin & Co (ECLP) controlling 75% of the industry. Centralisation and rationalisation of the china-clay industry is a process that has continued unabated to the present day, headed by English China Clays International (as ECLP became). Two independent producers survive: the Goonvean and Rostowrack Company, with pits at Goonvean, Rostowrack, Trelavour and Wheal Prosper; and Steetley Burke, who operate Greensplat and Bodelva.

Transport of the finished clay also saw many changes after 1918; the use of casks was phased out, and cooperages, once an indispensable part of the St Austell area, were closed. The availability of cheap motor-lorries after the Great War meant the end of the horse teams and their waggoners. Of the ports and harbours, Pentewan finally succumbed to its silt, and the railway closed; Charlestown retained some traffic, but Par and Fowey were now the principal china-clay harbours.

Iron winch at Pentewan harbour   Photo: CAU

NEW TECHNOLOGY FOR A NEW AGE

THE EFFECTS of the 1939 to 1945 war were particularly long-lasting, as many pits were closed in an attempt to streamline and rationalise the industry. Several of these war-time casualties remain abandoned to the present-day. China-clay production was now effectively in the hands of one large company, with such smaller ones as remained controlling only a handful of pits. Papermaking was now the principal market for china-clay, and the use of china-stone was in decline. A new mood was abroad; men were no longer so prepared to work long hours of back-breaking labour for little pay, and mechanisation could remove the need for a large workforce.

Another post-war influence was the rising price of coal. This rapidly made the use of the old Cornish beam engines uneconomic, and the remaining engines were rapidly replaced with electric pumps. The last engine to work in Cornwall was at Greensplat, in 1959. The high price of coal also meant the end of the pan-kiln; these were gradually replaced with oil-fired rotary driers, although a few kilns were converted to oil firing for a short time. The pan-kilns did not at first physically disappear, but their cold hearths and over-grown tanks hastened the demise of the brickworks too, as the special tiles and bricks were no longer needed. Another casualty of the post-war era was the china-stone mills, which had all ceased to work by 1965.

Rationalisation and efficiency was the order for the new age, and the aim has been to concentrate production in fewer but larger pits. Old pits were expanded and merged to become deep and extensive excavations, swallowing up earlier dumps and kilns in the process. Where scores of men had laboured in the stopes, now automatic monitors wash the clay, and even a large pit may have only three men on each shift. Separation of the waste sand and mica is now done by classifiers and hydro-cyclones, and the methods of dumping too have changed: the old conical tips have been outlawed in the wake of the Welsh Aberfan disaster. Lorries or conveyors now dump the sand and stent on flat topped benches, which are seeded to produce strange slab-sided green hills. A change of attitude toward the environment during the 1960s ended the disposal of mica wastes in rivers and streams, and today mica is impounded in huge lagoons or used to backfill old pits that have no potential for reworking.

The modern industry is now highly specialised and technical in every respect, able to produce grades of clay refined to suit any requirement, and would be unrecognisable to the old captains whose main concern was simply to keep the clay free of grit. Output now stands at some three million tons per year. While many recent changes in the industry have been beneficial both to the environment and the workforce, production at the present rate can only hasten the destruction of the remaining natural and historic landscapes. Farms and cottages are swallowed; hamlets and old mills have vanished under mica and sand; and the landscape of the early clay industry itself is now under threat, as pits, dumps, kilns and stacks created by the old clay companies are swept away.

China Clay train at Drinnick Mill, 1984 *John R Smith*

GAZETTEER

It is impossible to include every location associated with the china-clay industry in a book of this size, and the Gazetteer is a selection of the most interesting, best-preserved or otherwise significant remains. Dozens of others could have been included. The volatile nature of the landscape in the St Austell china-clay district will quickly make any selection such as this redundant, and the keen explorer must be prepared for some sites to have disappeared within the lifetime of this book. Nevertheless, many beautiful and interesting abandoned works are waiting for the reader to 'discover' them for the first time, just as I and others before me have been charmed by their magic in the past. Long may they continue to exert their fascination.

BUT PLEASE REMEMBER . . . . . .

All the sites listed in the Gazetteer are private property, and members of the public must have permission from the owners before visiting them. Wheal Martyn is of course open to the public during the season, and is not only a fine museum of the industry's development, but also an excellent historic site in its own right. Other sites may sometimes be visible from the public road or a footpath may run close by. It cannot be emphasised too strongly that *no-one should ever enter an active clay-works without permission and supervision*. Old workings, too, are potentially very dangerous places, with deep water, open shafts and other overgrown hazards.

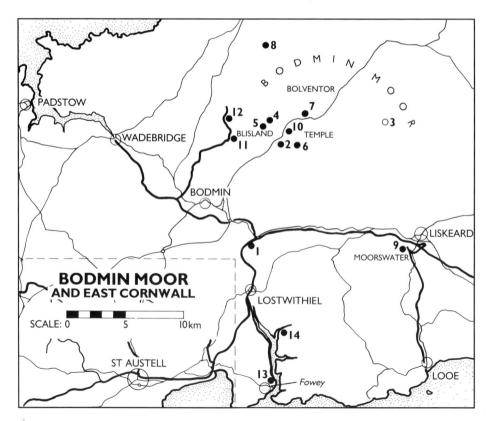

4: Durfold china-clay works, circa 1900   *Photo: ECCI*

1 BODMIN ROAD
SX 105638
Three large pan-kilns built beside the GWR main line, serving the clayworks at Glynn Valley. A direct rail connection was laid in from the western end of Bodmin Road station (now Bodmin Parkway). Overgrown and partly reused for other industrial purposes, the kilns have deteriorated rapidly in recent years.

2 BURNT HEATH
SX 128722
An amazingly well-preserved small clayworks, first worked in the 1870s, and closed by 1906. The pit, flat-topped dumps, and tiny process area are all typical of much older works on Hensbarrow, but here on Bodmin Moor the early technology lingered on into the 20th century. Next to the flooded pit is a small mica-drag, a set of round granite-faced settling pits, and rectangular settling tanks that served a small pan-kiln. The kiln survives only as two grassy platforms, which are the remains of the pan and linhay respectively.

3 CARKEET
SX 218732
Carkeet is the only brickworks on Bodmin Moor. The bricks made here were marked **LISKEARD** and can still be found in the area, although the brickworks was in operation only for a very short time around 1900. The site has the remains of a very small downdraught kiln with a superb square brick stack; there is also a drying shed, with a waterwheel pit at the rear. The waterwheel probably drove a pug-mill, used to mix the clay.

4 DURFOLD
SX 119738
Durfold was an early clayworks on Bodmin Moor, in operation by 1864. It was also one of the first to lay pipelines to the nearest railway, in this case to the kiln at Stump Oak Siding (Tresarret). This was done under Frank Parkyn's ownership after 1870. Parkyn was in the forefront of clay extraction on Bodmin Moor; born near Lerryn in 1850, son of a prosperous wool merchant, he was sent to

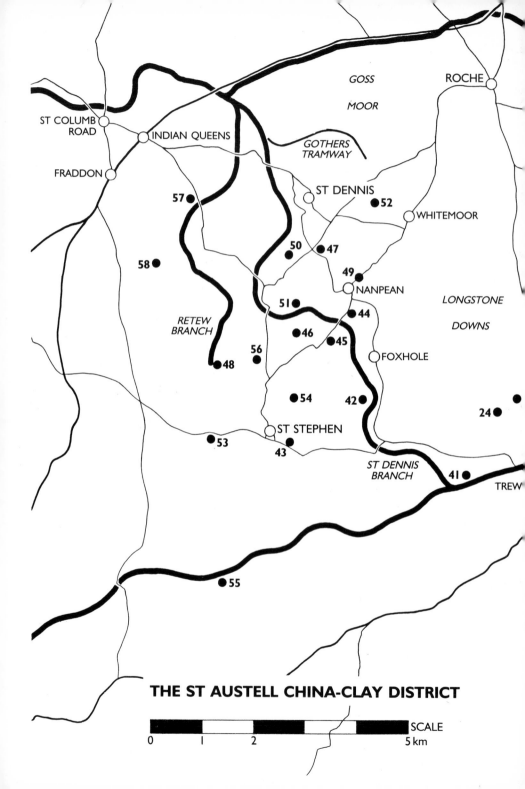

THE ST AUSTELL CHINA-CLAY DISTRICT

SCALE

0   1   2   5 km

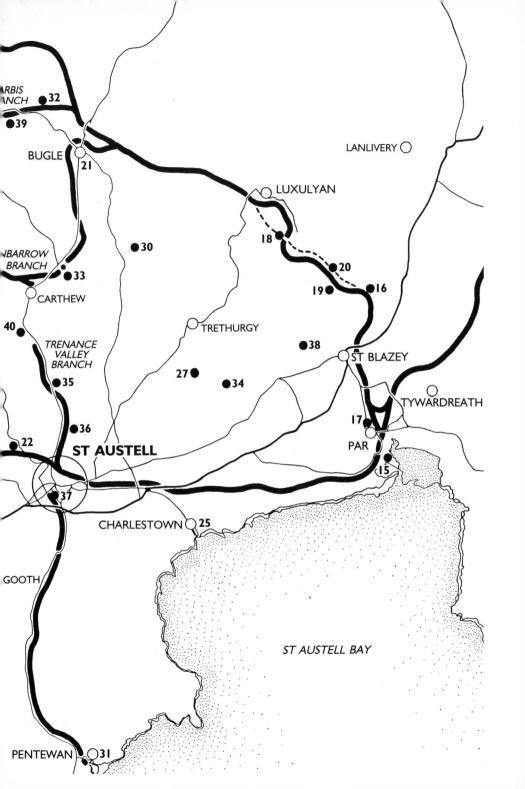

6: Glynn Valley china-clay works, Cardinham   *Photo: CAU*

live on the Moor as a child because of his delicate health. While there, he developed an interest in china-clay. He eventually owned the clayworks at Carwen, Durfold, Temple, Glynn Valley and Burnt Heath, and was able to indulge his passion for water-powered machinery on all these sites (see 5: Gawns Wheel, below). In 1884 he went into partnership with Woodman Peters, and the company of Parkyn & Peters went on to work larger pits on Hensbarrow at Halviggan, Biscovillet, and Blackpool. The pit here at Durfold has mica drags and settling pits that were fed by an adit from the pit.

5 GAWNS WHEEL
SX 113733

A leat was taken off the stream by a weir at Durfold; about a quarter of a mile to the south is the huge wheelpit for the Gawns Wheel. At 50 feet in diameter, this was amongst the largest ever erected in Cornwall. It was built by Frank Parkyn around 1919 to pump his clayworks at Temple, and transmitted its power one and a quarter miles across Trehudreth Downs by means of flat-rods. This extraordinary arrangement was not particularly successful, as much of the power was wasted in friction and lost motion. Parkyn scrapped the flat-rod system, and built a generator beside the wheel (the house for which can still be

seen). Wires then transmitted the current to Temple to operate electric pumps.

6 GLYNN VALLEY
SX 143718

This large and impressive site is the result of a very complex history. It was started in 1875, and was worked in four separate phases until it was closed in 1942, never to reopen. The clay

6: Mica-drags at Glynn Valley   *Photo: CAU*

7: Hawkstor china-clay works   *Photo: CAU*

was not of particularly good quality, having a high proportion of the white mica which is a common failing of the Bodmin Moor clays. The site today has a wide range of features, including the pit, sky-tips and finger dumps. Behind the sky-tips is the wheelpit used for pumping and winding. The process area has seen at least three phases of development, with the late mica-drags well preserved and impressive in their complexity. The pan-kiln to the south seems to have been planned to be twice its present size, but was never completed; the stack is remote and served by a long flue. In the last phase of working after 1919, the kiln became redundant and the clay was piped to new drys at Bodmin Road.

7 HAWKSTOR
SX 150745
The Bodmin Moor works that everyone knows beside the main A30 near Bolventor, Hawkstor is another site that has had a complex history. After 1929 the clay was piped south to kilns beside the GWR main line at Newbridge. The pit worked until 1971, and the dumps have been used in recent years to make concrete blocks.

8 HENNEWARD
SX 112800
Henneward was a very small pit, and worked intermittently from 1870 to 1914. The pan-kiln here belongs to the last phase of working, and is a classic example with its remote stack, settling tanks to the rear, and settling pits at a higher level again.

9 MOORSWATER
SX 235643
The old Liskeard and Caradon Railway's headquarters. Eventually this became the truncated northern stub of the GWR Looe branch, but still had a locomotive shed and small works until the 1960s. In 1906 the St Neot China Clay Company built new kilns here at Moorswater to serve their pit at Northwood, and a pipeline was laid across the moor to connect the two. Although the Northwood works closed in 1921, the pipeline to the kilns was taken over by the nearby Parsons Park pit; Park is still in operation today as part of ECCI Ltd, and so the site at Moorswater continues to be busy.

10 TEMPLE
SX 136732
Temple was never a very successful pit, but has a place in history due to its long association with Frank Parkyn. He worked it intermittently from 1876 until the 1920s, and during its last years power was provided for pumping by the Gawns Wheel. The wooden supports for the flat-rod system can still be seen in places on

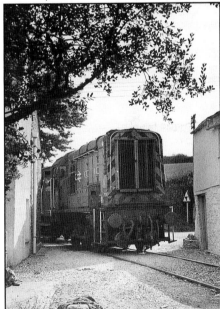

China-clay train on the Wenford Branch at Helland Bridge   *Photo: John R Smith*

12: Pan-kilns at Wenford (Poleys Bridge)   *Photo: CAU*

Trehudreth Downs. At Temple the flooded pits and dumps are now very overgrown, but in amongst the gorse are two wheelpits, remains of an engine house and shaft, and the leat systems that supplied the works.

11 TRESARRET (STUMP OAK)
SX 089726
A kiln was built here beside the old Bodmin and Wadebridge Railway to serve Parkyn's pit at Durfold. Stump Oak Siding was in use from about 1880, and the site is now easily accessible from the Camel Trail footpath and cycleway. The pan-kiln, though very overgrown, has all its features intact except for the

stack, and at the rear there is a group of particularly fine settling tanks.

12 WENFORD
SX 085744
The impressive line of kilns here dates from 1906, when the pit at Stannon was reopened. Stannon, with Parsons Park (see 9: Moorswater), is still a major producer for ECCI, and so the works continue to be busy. The kilns have been converted to house modern drying and storage plant. Until 1983 they were served by the rail link up the Wenford Branch, the clay going via Bodmin Road and Lostwithiel to Fowey for shipment.

FOWEY ESTUARY

13 CARNE POINT
SX 128525
Fowey was developed as a deep-water china-clay port after 1870, when it was connected by rail to Lostwithiel, and in 1874 to Par. New jetties and sidings were built by the Great Western Railway, and the quays at Carne Point became the principal destination for Cornish clay, today handling over 1.5 million tons a year, 55 percent of total exports. The best views of the docks are obtained from the river or from the footpath that runs from

Bodinnick to Mixtow Pill on the opposite bank. The quays at Carne Point only had rail access until 1968, when the Par line was closed and converted into a private road for ECCI lorries.

14 LERRYN
SX 135568
Here in the woods on the southern shore of the creek is the remains of an extraordinary riverside park, laid out by Frank Parkyn as a gift to his birthplace. Parkyn lived for many years at Golant across the river; he organised the

Regatta and involved himself in the village life of Lerryn. The park is now overgrown and neglected, but paths still lead to curious fragments of walls and a pond, now dry, which looks to have had a clay settling pit as its direct inspiration.

13: Carne Point docks, Fowey, with steamers loading china-clay, circa 1910 *Photo: Redruth Local Studies Library*

LUXULYAN VALLEY

The Luxulyan Valley is remarkable for many things, only some of which are connected with china-clay; J T Treffry's new harbour at Par and the tramway system inland were initially built to carry copper ore and granite. As copper declined, so china-clay and stone assumed a greater importance, and these 'new' minerals ensured the survival of much of Treffry's work into this century.

15 PAR
SX 075530

Started in the mid-1820s, Par continues to be an important harbour. By the 1850s it included not only the quays but a lead smelter, a granite dressing yard, sawmills, shipbuilding yards and a candle factory. A brickworks was also established after 1880. The remains of all these were swept away in a great redevelopment of the 1960s, when the modern clay processing equipment we see today was installed. On the opposite side of the Par to St Austell road is a line of late-period pan-kilns, some still in use as clay stores. The brick inlay on one stack reads '(Par)kyn & Peters'. These kilns were served by a branch of the harbour railway, which in later years operated two strangely squat Bagnall saddle tanks, due to a very low bridge. *Judy* is now at Wheal Martyn Museum, while *Alfred*, last to work at Par in 1977, is still in steam on the Bodmin Steam Railway; they were featured in one of the Rev. Awdrey's children's books.

15: Pan-kiln furnace room at Par   Photo: CAU

16 PONTS MILL
SX 073562

The hub of Treffry's transport system, Ponts Mill was in medieval times the highest navigable point on the Par river. The silt washed down from tin streamworks on the Hensbarrow moors has turned the estuary into meadows. Prominent now is the modern ECCI clay processing plant, built on the site of an older kiln and still served by a rail connection off the route of the tramway. Everywhere there are relics of Treffry's trans-peninsular dream: the overgrown canal basin, the river Par diverted behind a massive embankment, and the foot of the Carmears inclined plane. Ponts Mill was, from 1870, the setting for the largest complex of china-stone mills in Cornwall. These were demolished after closure in the 1960s, leaving only fragments of masonry. Only the pan-kiln attached to the mills can still be seen, with its settling tanks to the rear.

17 ST BLAZEY
SX 071546

Hidden in the middle of the village is the mellow brick headquarters of the Cornwall Minerals Railway. Built for the Company by Sir Morton Peto in 1872-4, it features a semi-roundhouse locomotive shed with turntable feeding nine shed roads, erecting shop, machine shop, and forge with its square brick stack. The depot was in use until recent years to house BR's modern locomotives, but has now been converted to light industrial units.

17: The St Blazey Depot of the Cornwall Minerals Railway   Photo: CAU

18: Treffry Viaduct / Aquaduct, in the Luxulyan Valley   Photo: John R Smith

18 TREFFRY VIADUCT

SX 057572

This finely proportioned viaduct was built for Treffry between 1839 and 1842 by the local granite masons of Luxulyan. It opened up a direct rail link from the china-clay pits of Hensbarrow to the new port of Par, as the line continued through Luxulyan to Bugle. The viaduct, 89 feet high and of ten arches, is also an aqueduct carrying a leat beneath the trackbed.

19 TREVANNY DRY

SX 065563

This pan-kiln was built in the 1920s by the Central Cornwall Company, who had a small pit on Starrick Moor. The clay was piped down to the kiln, which was served by a railway from Ponts Mill along the bottom of the valley. All the features of a late period kiln are well-preserved, and it is possible to see how it was later modified for use with a filter-press.

20 WHEELPIT MILL

SX 066566

After the Carmears incline was closed in 1874 following the construction of the new railway through the valley, the wheelpit at the top of the incline became redundant. Around 1890 a china-stone mill was built on either side of the pit, and a new 40 foot wheel installed to drive it. The mill worked until 1914, and contains not only the grinding pans but most of the heavy shafts and gears. The ground stone was sent down a pipeline to the kiln at Ponts Mill.

21: Bugle in the early 1900s   *Photo: CAU*

21 BUGLE
SX 015591

A village wholly created by the china-clay industry, Bugle grew up around its coaching inn. When Treffry's tramway arrived in the 1840s, there was only a farm at Molinnis and the public house. Now it is dominated by the towering dumps that overshadow the terraces built by the clay companies to house their workforce. The railway to Newquay from Par survives for the moment, and the trackbed for the Wheal Rose branch and the Goonbarrow branch (both lifted) can still be traced by the determined, although later development has obscured the lines in places.

22 CARANCARROW KILN
SX 004531

Two kilns were built on Trenance Siding, served from the GWR main line. The westernmost, now very overgrown, is the Carancarrow Kiln. This is an excellent example of a late 19th century kiln at its most mature, which replaced an earlier, smaller kiln on the same site. To the rear is an extensive range of mica-drags, settling pits and tanks, all built of stone with a maze of pipes, walkways and channels hidden in dense vegetation.

23 CARBIS BRICKWORKS
SX 001595

Sadly now part of an industrial slum, Carbis is a wonderful example of a small Cornish brickworks. In operation from 1883, it produced thousands of refractory bricks and tiles, which can be found throughout mid-Cornwall. The square brick stack provided the draught for three cupola or 'beehive' kilns, of which there is only one other example in the county. Next door is the Wheal Prosper Kiln. The view from here down to Bugle is of a skyline punctuated by pan-kiln stacks.

32: Carbis brickworks   *Photo: CAU*

24 CARNESTENTS
SW 990538

Carnestents is a good example of a tin streamworks that became a china-clay works, and is part of the Gover Valley complex. At the eastern end are the ruinous remains of two kilns, which belong to the earlier phase of extraction; above and to the west is an overgrown and intricate complex of pits and dumps, now a hunting ground for foxes and buzzards. The later process area for Carnestents is further down the Gover Valley at **SW 996535**, where leats from the pit fed the clay stream into a labyrinthine group of settling tanks. In amongst this maze of granite walls is the kiln, part of which is now a kennels.

25 CHARLESTOWN
SX 038518

The little port is today much as Charles Rashleigh left it; there has been very little modern development to spoil the ambience of a late 18th century harbour and village.

Charlestown is distinctive and not yet part of St Austell, though separated only by a few fields. Clay is still shipped from here, mostly by the Goonvean and Rostowrack company, and the fortunate visitor may see a coasting vessel leaving the harbour on the flood tide. The chutes on the east quay are used by lorries to load the boats. A similar arrangement was used to load the clay from Lovering's kiln, which can be seen to the north of the dock; this

25: Charlestown Harbour   *Photo: John R Smith*

processed clay fed from Carclaze pit by pipeline. An underground tramway from the linhay of the kiln brought the clay out high above the ships on the east quay. On the road to St Austell is the Charlestown Foundry, one the few iron-foundries still active in the county. Now part of ECCI, it produces castings for the clay industry.

26 FOREST
SW 998535

The clay pit is hidden behind rhododendron covered dumps, and very difficult to approach; the best views of Forest as a landscape feature are from above, when its importance as part of the Gover Valley is clear. Beneath the GWR viaduct to the south are the kilns; the earliest and most interesting beneath the bridge, with its later replacement higher upslope. The old kiln is tiny and very atmospheric. Its tanks at the rear must have soon proved hopelessly inadequate, and they have been extended in a piecemeal fashion to one side, making the dry-men's job very difficult.

27 GARKER
SX 040546

A pit typical of the early system of extensive working; the clay has been extracted through-out the valley floor, leaving a complex and overgrown maze of shallow pits and dumps. At the lower end are two pan-kilns that are not in fact associated with this pit, but processed clay from Trethurgy and Vounder. Garker was in operation by 1863, and was later owned by Parkyn & Peters; it closed in 1942.

28 GOVER VALLEY
SW 995540

The Gover Valley is an outdoor museum of the mid-period china-clay industry in a rural setting. The fast-flowing Gover Stream rushes down its rocky bed to St Austell, surrounded on all sides by rhododendrons and oak woodland. The steep valley is crowded with abandoned pits, dumps, kilns, and leat systems, all now returning to nature; this is perhaps the essence of Hensbarrow, a hundred years ago. Within the valley are several important works: Forest, abandoned in 1942; Gover, now a sheer gash in the hillside; Carnestents; and Wheal Jacob, worked for tin and china-clay. At the lower end is the Great Western Railway viaduct of 1898, which replaced the original timber Cornwall Railway structure.

29 GREENSPLAT ENGINE HOUSE
SW 996554

A small engine house beside the Greensplat works, an independent pit not owned by ECCI. Although it contained only a 30 inch engine, it is distinguished by being the last beam pumping engine to work in Cornwall.

28: An air-dry and pan-kiln in the Gover Valley, around 1900   *Photo: Wheal Martyn Museum*

Re-erected on this site in 1887 after conversion from a rotative engine, it pumped the pit until February 1959. The beam engine was removed from the house in 1972 and can now be seen at the Poldark museum, near Helston.

30 LANTERN
SX 025570

There are very few well-preserved complete china-clay works such as this in the St Austell area–with flooded pit, dumps and process area–all now overgrown but unchanged since closure in 1942. Behind the pit are ruins of the pumping engine, boiler house, and settling pits and the shell of a large mid-period pan-kiln.

31 PENTEWAN
SX 020472

Pentewan today is an uncomfortable mixture of old and new; the overgrown and silted remains of Hawkins' harbour lie tucked into the eastern corner of the beach, almost overwhelmed by holiday chalets, caravans, and all the cheap paraphernalia of the tourist trade. The inner harbour still has its water and the elevated track of the railway survives, bringing to mind the faded sepia images of the little port in its heyday. It is only on the beach that the visitor can appreciate the desperate problems involved in keeping this refuge open; where ships were once warped into the entrance, now there are only great banks of

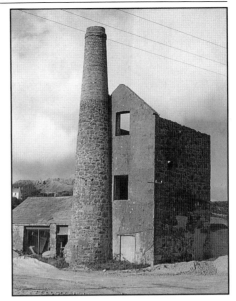

29: Greensplat engine house   *Photo: CAU*

sand. As early as 1907 this sand was used in the manufacture of concrete building blocks–still an important use for china clay waste–and after the closure of the Pentewan Railway track was relaid in the block works. Fragments of rail, two cast-iron winches, and the inner harbour gates are reminders that the last clay shipment left in 1929.

30: Lantern china-clay works   *Photo: CAU*

31: The inner harbour gates at Pentewan

Photo: CAU

32 ROSEMELLYN

SX 009601

By 1878 Rosemellyn was a very rich pit, with four steam engines on the works. Owned by North and Rose, its clay was of high quality and always commanded an excellent price. The pan-kiln, set back from the road at **SX 006597**, is a magnificent example dating from the 1870s with a cut granite stack that is now sadly leaning away from the vertical. At the rear of the pit is the one surviving engine house.

33 STENALEES TUNNEL

SX 013567

Part of the Goonbarrow Branch, built by the Cornwall Minerals Railway. Opened in 1893, the line was run independently by the CMR for three years until it was absorbed by the Great Western. Steeply graded and with sharp curves, the branch was always difficult to work; as the pan-kilns below Goonbarrow and Gunheath closed in the 1950s, so traffic dwindled and the line closed in 1965. The tunnel is 341 yards long, and remains open though very wet.

34 TREGREHAN KILN

SX 043543

An unusual and interesting little kiln, buried in the undergrowth beside the road north of Tregrehan Mills. It is a good example of a kiln

that was intended to be larger, but never grew to match its owner's aspirations. The stack has been built some distance to the north and connected to the pan by a long flue, to allow for later extension of the kiln. At the rear, granite tanks are cut into the steep hillside. They were fed by a leat carrying the clay stream from a pit on the other side of the hill; this arrangement, usual in the 1860s and 70s before pipelines were common, is rarely found intact on Hensbarrow.

35 TRENANCE VALLEY

SX 011529 to 005560

Perhaps the most vital thoroughfare on Hensbarrow, this valley leads directly to Charlestown and Pentewan from the pits above St Austell. Millions of tons of clay must have passed this way. The railway through the valley was not opened until 1920, though planned much earlier; by then there was already a proliferation of kilns all the way to Carthew, serving pits on the slopes above. Clayworks within the valley include Trethowel, Boskell, Ruddle with its perfect enclosing sky-tips, Lansalson and Gomm. Today the road from St Austell to Stenalees is a splendid introduction to Hensbarrow, passing under the railway viaduct and through the lush Menacuddle Woods before making the long climb to Carthew. There are pan-kiln stacks on all sides,

36: Lovering's pan-kiln at Trethowel   Photo: John R Smith

overgrown dumps, and everywhere the sound of rushing water amid rhododendrons.

36 TRETHOWEL KILN
SX 013535

Once this massive kiln, the largest ever built, dominated the hillside above Trethowel. Even now with its roof stripped it remains an impressive sight. Completed in February 1921, the pan-kiln was built by John Lovering to serve his works at Higher and Lower Ninestones; to increase capacity, two pans abutted a central furnace room and coal store, with square stacks at either end. As the largest and most symmetrical of its kind, Trethowel is eloquent in decay. Kilns such as this are rarely suitable for adaptive reuse, and their fate is uncertain; perhaps they will ultimately be recognised as important monuments to a vanished technology.

37 WEST HILL CLAY CELLARS
SX 011522

Here, almost lost in the middle of a supermarket car-park, is the clay store or cellars of the Pentewan Railway. Clay carted down from Hensbarrow was stored in this little building before being transhipped to railway wagons. All around was the cramped West Hill Depot, with gas-works, coal stores, and the St Austell Foundry, later an outpost of William West's establishment at St Blazey.

Nothing remains of this industrial complex but the clay cellars, ignored by the shoppers as they push their wire trolleys to waiting cars, now parked where *Canopus* and *Pioneer* once ran.

38 WHEAL RASHLEIGH
SX 060551

Overgrown dumps surround two flooded pits, now used by a local angling club. In the easternmost is a half-submerged waterwheel, a last reminder of the industrial nature of this now apparently natural landscape. Active in 1858, Rashleigh's kilns are to the east on the

37: Pentewan Railway clay-cellars, West Hill, St Austell   Photo: CAU

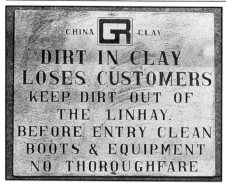

39: Sign at Wheal Prosper kiln, Carbis   *CAU*

road to St Blazey; the original kiln is hidden to the rear, and ranks with the oldest survivors in the St Austell area.

39 WHEAL PROSPER KILN
SX 001596

Beside the road at Carbis, this is the last working pan-kiln in the Hensbarrow granite and the last coal-fired kiln in the county. That it should survive as a working kiln is due entirely to its ownership by the Goonvean and Rostowrack Company (who have had limited resources to invest in new plant); this happy accident of fate allows the enthusiast to enjoy the sight of one smoking chimney amongst the forest of dead stacks that line the road to Bugle. The kiln still has its magnificent slate roof, unlike so many that were replaced with corrugated iron, and has been modernised only by the addition of a filter press at the rear. This is the terminus of the Carbis Branch, once part of the Cornwall Minerals Railway; the line is still open but sees little traffic. Wheal Prosper pit is expanding, and the kiln may soon be replaced by a modern drying plant.

40 WHEAL MARTYN
SX 005554

The Wheal Martyn Museum actually incorporates the processing areas of three clayworks; Gomm, Wheal Martyn, and a micaworks that reprocessed waste from pits higher up the valley. Now combined into one splendid display with outdoor and indoor exhibitions, a visit to Wheal Martyn is essential to an understanding of the industry. There are two working waterwheels (one driving a lift pump), mica-drags, and a display housed inside a well restored pan-kiln. Various outdoor exhibits include railway locomotives, carts and a Peerless lorry. The Gomm kiln at the entrance to the site is an unusual survival in the St Austell area, with its double-ridge roof gables and granite supports for the linhay.

40: The main entrance of Wheal Martyn Museum, formerly the Gomm kiln and linhay   *Photo: CAU*

41 BURNGULLOW
SW 985525

A line of pan-kilns nearly a quarter of a mile long was built here by Parkyn and Peters in the early 1900s to serve their pit at Blackpool. The modern clay stores and silos which replaced the kilns mean that Burngullow is still a busy rail loading point for ECCI; there was also a passenger station, and an engine shed for the locomotive that worked the branch to Drinnick. At **SW 980524** are two remaining pan-kilns, one of which has the initials 'FP' and the date 1929 on its stack: another reminder of Frank Parkyn's presence here.

42 CARPALLA ENGINE HOUSE
SW 963539

Standing beside the flooded pit that has been used to store mica waste, this house is unusual in having an intact roof. It contained a 40 inch engine that was moved here from West Wheal Kitty (St Agnes) in 1915; this date perhaps explains the slightly self-conscious architectural detailing, not at all like the 'classic' Cornish engine house. The engine was replaced by electric pumps in 1944 and put in store at the Science Museum. There are hopes that it might one day come back to Cornwall.

43 CHAPEL MILL
SW 948531

A marvellously atmospheric example of a Cornish stone mill, now almost hidden from the casual glance by vegetation, yet only a few yards from the main road on the outskirts of St Stephen. Chapel Mill is not as imposing as the Tregargus mills, but very important in that it is the only one to have all its machinery intact, including the waterwheel, underdrift gears, and pans. At the rear are a set of diminutive tanks and the pan-kiln for drying the ground stone.

44 DRINNICK MILL
SW 961558

The very antithesis of the popular image of Cornwall, Drinnick is a grey sprawl of chimneys, tanks and interlacing railway lines surrounded by the sky-tips of older workings. It is perhaps best appreciated on a wet, misty Cornish afternoon. Rail traffic is still important

44: Drinnick Power Station   *Photo: John R Smith*

here, and the wharf has its granite sett surface intact with the ruins of the weighbridge at the rear. The power station at **SW 958553** was built in 1936 to serve the industry; fascinating for its ugliness, it is now disused and one of the last coal-fired stations of this size in the country.

45 GOONAMARRIS KILN
SW 956551

South of Drinnick, this is a very complete pan-kiln, almost lost in enclosing willows. It served the Goonamarris pit, also known as Luke's Goonamarris; the kiln is narrow across the pan, with remains of the travelling bridge and a superb assemblage of tanks and pits to the rear, all built in granite.

46 GOONVEAN
SW 949552

Goonvean is an old pit and was active in the 1790s. The pit today is still an important producer, but unlike most other survivors from this period has a wealth of historic features grouped on the eastern rim of the pit. At **SW 948554** is the old Goonvean engine house, with its boiler house and stack intact. In 1910 this was replaced by the new engine house at the entrance to the works, which remarkably survives with the engine still inside. The house is splendid enough, perhaps the very best in the St Austell area with its balance bob pit and

46: Goonvean engine house with pan-kilns and the old engine house behind   *Photo: John R Smith*

shaft to the front; inside is the Harvey's 50 inch engine of 1863, which had worked at two mines in St Agnes before re-erection here. The engine ceased to work in 1955; sadly recent gale damage has destroyed the roof and left the contents open to the elements. Between the two engine houses are a remarkable pair of pan-kilns, which were served by a branch from the CMR mineral line to St Dennis. They are of the same period as the new engine, and the whole group is of great historic importance.

47 OLD HENDRA
SW 953569

This works is another early site, once owned by J T Treffry. Today there is only the abandoned pit, but the archaeological interest

47: Hendra china-clay works   *Photo: CAU*

48: Meledor crossing on the Retew branch, 1983 *Photo: K Burdett*

lies to the north-west where the Hendra Incline of Treffry's tramway system can still be traced on the ground. At **SW 958568** is the engine house belonging to the later Hendra works, now a large flooded pit in use as a reservoir by ECCI.

48 MELBUR AND RETEW BRANCH
SW 933546

At the end of a narrow lane is the Melbur terminus of the Retew Branch. Extended to this point in 1912, the branch was closed and lifted in 1983 but the wharfs and crossing gates remain. Hidden in the bushes close by is a delightful waterwheel. The trackbed of the branch provides a very interesting walk through the Fal Valley, but permission must be sought from ECCI first.

49: Currian Road, Nanpean *Photo: CAU*

49 NANPEAN HOUSING
SW 962563

An outstanding example of purpose-built industrial housing, Currian Road in Nanpean is a set of intimidating terraces built in the early 1900s. Today the visual symmetry of the design has been marred by the insertion of modern windows; conferring some benefits of prestige and comfort on the inhabitants, no doubt, but sadly diminishing the integrity of the whole.

50 PARKANDILLACK
SW 948568

The St Austell china-clay district is very fortunate in having two Cornish beam engines still in their houses; one is at Goonvean, the other here, at Parkandillack. Happily this engine is conserved in its house by ECCI, and is looked after by a band of volunteers. Not only does the site have its boiler house intact, but also a complete example of mica-drags and settling pits at the rear. The remainder of the works is now modern driers, calciners and bagging plant, and continues to be a busy railhead.

51 SLIP
SW 950556

Slip is a crossroads of sorts, where the road from Goonvean meets the railway from Drinnick. A strange, neglected spot, yet here there are a few cottages and all around the

50: Parkandillack engine house   *Photo: CAU*

51: The 'blondin' at Slip   *Photo: CAU*

debris of a lost age. Slip Quarry was an important producer of china-stone; the **Blondin**, or aerial ropeway is still kept in working order so that pumps below can be maintained. The siding that served the quarry is now overgrown but the Wharf survives; the remains of the china-stone crushing plant are on the opposite side of the 'main' line. To the north, at **SW 949558**, is the Rostowrack pan-kiln, which is distinguished by having an underground tramway running from the base of its linhay through a tunnel under the road to the siding opposite.

52 ST DENNIS CONSOLS AND GOTHERS

SW 965578

An example of an upland china-clay landscape as it was before 1939; few remain in the St Austell area. There are three clayworks here: St Dennis Consols, Gothers, and Wheal Frederick. Pochin owned Gothers, and linked it to Domellick Siding on the CMR St Dennis line by means of a tramway, built in 1879. All were closed by 1942. Today the downs are an attractive mix of little dumps and flooded pits, with the engine house of Consols at

SW 964577. At SW 964584 to the north are two remarkable little kilns; both are of early form, with small tanks. The easternmost formed the terminus of the tramway, which was worked by a small steam locomotive.

53: Terras china-stone mill   *Photo: CAU*

53 TERRAS

SW 934532

A china-stone mill right beside the road on the way out of St Stephen. The impressive building with its russet iron roof and rustic stack is not of course the mill, but the pan-kiln that served it; the mill is behind, now used as a barn by the farmer. No machinery remains inside.

54 TREGARGUS AND WHEAL ARTHUR

SW 948537 to 950545

The Goonabarn Valley was noted for its china-stone quarries and mills; all had ceased work by 1965, but there are extensive remains of a unique industry in this hidden valley. At the southern end is the lower Tregargus mill, solid and well proportioned and still with most of its roof. A tramway brought the stone down from the quarries into the rear of the building. In amongst the trees is Trevear Mill, with its

54: Tregargus china-stone mill, 1984   *John R Smith*

miller's cottage to one side. This had a tiny attached pan-kiln, which is now difficult to see amidst the enclosing brambles; a flue leads to a

54: Installing the wheel at Tregargus mill   *Photo: Wheal Martyn Museum*

52: Trenowth china-stone mill in the 1920s

Photo: Wheal Martyn Museum

pygmy stack up on the hill above. The pans survive within the mill, and there is a wonderful flying brick arch that supported the launder to the wheel. The function of this may be better appreciated at Tregargus Mill, further up the path; here the waterwheel is still in place, though now very decrepit. This mill is almost overwhelmed by recent dumping of waste that has now filled the stone quarries above. There were at one time four mills here, which indicates how important the stone industry was after 1870. An interesting walk, with the Barn River rushing close below, leads to Wheal Arthur, where a large pan-kiln completely overshadows its attached stone-mill on the northern end. The mill is difficult to approach, but still contains its waterwheel. Behind is the quarry, now an overgrown and secret place.

55 TRENOWTH
SW 936505

A stone-mill well off the granite, hidden in the bottom of a sylvan valley at Trenowth. The leat that served it first fed the very tall corn mill, now converted to a dwelling, and then flowed under the road. The stone-mill is perhaps the most unusual in the area, very derelict and overgrown but still impressive with its tailraces that discharge into a central sunken canal. On the eastern side are two tiny pan-kilns. At **SW 938507** is another, larger

pan-kiln of the late 1900s; this was built to serve another stone-mill at Combe Vale which is now demolished.

56 TRETHOSA SCHOOL AND CHAPEL
SW 944550 and 943546

The small farming hamlet of Trethosa became isolated in the middle of an industrial landscape during the late 19th century. A new workforce demanded new housing, and the nearby village of Treviscoe was transformed by rows of terraced houses into the Cornish equivalent of Merthyr or the Rhondda. The workers who went each morning to Kernick or Trethosa pit were staunchly non-conformist, and their families were large; the school and chapel thus became the focus for their spiritual and educational needs. The school is now closed, and awaits an uncertain fate; it is a classic example of a village school of the period, finely built in granite and segregated into separate halves for girls and boys. Trethosa chapel, gaunt and grey like the landscape that produced it, has a brooding presence over the valley where Kernick Mill is buried and across to Meledor, once a village too but now only a memory and a name.

57 WHEAL REMFREY BRICKWORKS
SW 936586

Brickworks seem to attract dereliction of the worst kind, and Remfrey was no exception;

once an important producer of bricks and tiles for the industry it became an area of fly-tipping and wind-blown refuse. The owning company's well-intentioned response has been to regrade the area, burying the well-preserved Newcastle kiln; two excellent brick stacks survive, for the present. At Trerice bridge just below, the Retew Branch crossed the road on the level and there was a siding into the brickworks.

56: Trethosa chapel   *Photo: John R Smith*

58 WHEAL BENALLACK
SW 923568 to 923565
There are actually two clayworks here, Wheal Benallack and New Halwyn, their pits combined into one flooded quarry. The surroundings are now completely overgrown with dense willow scrub, but hidden in this jungle are two engine houses (one remarkably on the top of a dump) and some excellent settling pits attached to mica drags. Dominating the site is the perfect New Halwyn sky-tip.

PENRYN

59 KERGILLIACK STONE MILLS
SW 782340
Stone mills are a surprise near Penryn, well outside the St Austell area, but there was china-stone in the quarries nearby and for a while it was ground here. There were three mills stepped down the hillside, the tailrace of one feeding the next. The uppermost mill is largely demolished, its remains now incorporated into a car repair yard; on the opposite side of the lane the next mill is well-preserved, with a broad central wheel-pit. Lower down the field, lost in an enclosing jungle of trees and scrub, is the third mill; this has a small pan-kiln attached with granite settling tanks and stack.

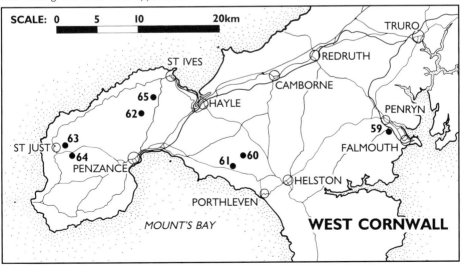

SCALE: 0   5   10   20km

TRURO
REDRUTH
ST IVES
CAMBORNE
HAYLE
65
62
PENRYN
59
63
ST JUST
64
PENZANCE
FALMOUTH
61   60
HELSTON
PORTHLEVEN
MOUNT'S BAY   **WEST CORNWALL**

TREGONNING HILL

Although Tregonning Hill was the area where Cookworthy had first prospected for china-clay and stone, the deposits proved too limited for sustained commercial exploitation. They were worked intermittently throughout the 19th century, leases changing hands in 1827, 1832, 1851 and 1863. None of these ventures was attended by any great success, but all contributed to the present-day pock-marked appearance of the Hill. The small amounts of china-clay and stone produced were shipped out through the convenient harbour of Porthleven, which would doubtless have become an important outlet for the industry if the setts had proved richer. In the 1870s a new consortium led by William Argall took over Tregonning Hill and Wheal Grey. Both of these works proved again to be poor in depth, and brickmaking provided the main source of income. By 1905 all the pits in this area were closed.

60 TREGONNING HILL
SW 604297
The Hill is scarred by small quarries and their associated dumps throughout its length; most of these are small-scale workings for china-stone. On the north-eastern slope is the overgrown shallow pit and dumps of the Tregonning Hill clayworks; in a field below stands a small downdraught brick kiln, now the only structure remaining from Argall's ownership.

61 WHEAL GREY
SW 594291
The flooded pit is used by a local angling club, and the surrounding dumps have returned to nature. At the entrance to the pit is the pan-kiln, which has a fine stack but is now so overgrown as to be almost invisible. On the opposite side of the pit at **SW595290** is a splendid little engine house, with its boiler house and stack intact.

60: Tregonning Hill brick kiln

Photo: CAU

Although there are localised deposits of china-clay in the West Penwith granite, these have never proved to be sufficiently extensive or of high enough quality for commercial success. This accident of geological history has undoubtedly spared the peninsula from the same fate as befell the Hensbarrow uplands; china-clay was being worked in Penwith by the 1830s, but even at this date there were difficulties in settling and processing the clay. Later workings were sporadic and largely unsuccessful, concentrated after 1914 in the St Just area at Leswidden and south-west of St Ives at Porthia and Baker's. Today there is only one active pit, at Bostraze near St Just.

62 BAKER'S PIT
SW 480357

Two small pits hidden in the valley below Castle-an-Dinas. The engine house is very unusual in that it once contained an indoor beam engine, rare in Cornwall and particularly rare on a clayworks. The boiler house alongside is well preserved, but the engine house itself has been greatly modified for reuse

61: Wheal Grey engine house, Tregonning Hill CAU

by an electric winder in later years. To the east is a very overgrown set of micas and settling pits, which served a small pan-kiln on the lane below. This can be identified only by its stack, but the rest of the kiln survives although completely hidden in an enclosing jungle of rhododendron and Japanese knotweed. Baker's closed in 1942.

63 BOSTRAZE
SW 385316

Bostraze is the only active works in Penwith, and is included here because it still uses a traditional pan-kin to dry the clay, although this is of recent design and is oil-fired.

64 LESWIDDEN
SW 393310

Leswidden also includes the Balleswidden works, which were restarted in 1913 on the site of earlier workings and considerably expanded during the 1920s. Beside the Penzance to St Just road, the most obvious remains are two gaunt pan-kilns built from concrete with little to recommend them as landscape features. The kiln on the south side of the road has been rebuilt and incorporates an earlier structure; that on the north side is later, and is purpose-built in an industrial style that has no direct counterpart on Hensbarrow. Both are served by well-designed mica-drag and settling-pit complexes upslope. The pit itself is flooded, and the dumps are being reworked for the manufacture of concrete blocks. To the south at **SW 389305** is a much earlier kiln with a tramming road between the tanks and the pan.

65 PENDERLEATH
SW 498378

Near St Ives, Penderleath was opened in 1923 and is surrounded by abandoned tin-mines.

The pit is flooded, and seems to have been located in poor ground; the pan-kiln lies some distance downhill and is easily identified by its tall, elegant stack. The stack is perhaps the best feature of the site and has a fine cut granite base with fully two-thirds of its height in brick,

an interesting reversal of the norm. The rest of the kiln follows the general pattern for the county, but unusually has had a double ridge roof; it has been reused for agricultural purposes since the clayworks closed in the 1930s, and is now derelict.

Loading china-clay at Penzance, in the early 1900s

Photo: ECCI

FURTHER READING

Barton, R M — *A History of the Cornish China-Clay Industry,* D Bradford Barton, 1966

Bray, P — *Around and About Clay Country,* Corran Publications, 1988

Cock, D — *A Treatise on . . . China Clay,* Simpkin Marshall, 1880

Herring, P & Smith, J R — *The Archaeology of the St Austell China-Clay Area,* Cornwall Archaeological Unit, 1991

Kittridge, A — *Cornwall's Maritime Heritage,* Twelveheads Press, 1989

Lewis, M J T — *The Pentewan Railway,* Twelveheads Press, 1981

Sharpe, A & Smith, J R — *Chapel Mill,* Cornwall Archaeological Unit, 1985

Smith, J R — *The Luxulyan Valley,* Cornwall Archaeological Unit, 1988

Stengelhofen, J P — *Wheal Martyn Museum Guide,* St Austell China Clay Museum Ltd, 1983

Varcoe, P — *China Clay: The Early Years,* Francis Antony, 1978

Vaughan, J — *An Illustrated History of West Country China Clay Trains,* Oxford Publishing Company,

ISBN 0 906294 25 8   © Cornwall Archaeological Unit 1992
First published 1992 by Twelveheads Press, Chy Mengleth, Twelveheads, Truro, Cornwall TR4 8SN